Breast Cancer Healing Scriptures

Guided Journal

*All scriptures are taken from the New International Version of the Bible unless noted.

Dedication

I dedicate this journal to all who have loved and lost. To the ones that are still in the fight. Never give up.

Love,

- Beryl

Introduction

Dear Warrior,
I created this journal to encourage you during your circumstance. A breast cancer diagnosis can be scary, uncertain, and downright earth shattering. I know for me it changed my world. I didn't know what to do; I was dumbfounded. I never thought I would be on the receiving end hearing the words you have breast cancer.

However, I have great news. You don't have to go through this process alone. This interactive breast cancer journal will help you walk through your journey surrounded by peace, love, and hope. You will find healing scriptures that will uplift you in the time of uncertainty, anxiety and doubt. There is a section where you can write your reflections about the scripture or write about how you are feeling. There is no right or wrong way to use this journal. My prayer is that this journal will help you overcome your fears, anxiety and that the love of God will keep you grounded in his peace.

Forever grateful,

Beryl

"But he was wounded for
our transgressions, He was
bruised for our iniquities;
The chastisement for our
peace was upon Him, And
by his stripes we are
healed."

Isaiah 53:5 (NKJV)

YOU ARE HEALED

What do you believe? Why? Write your thoughts below.

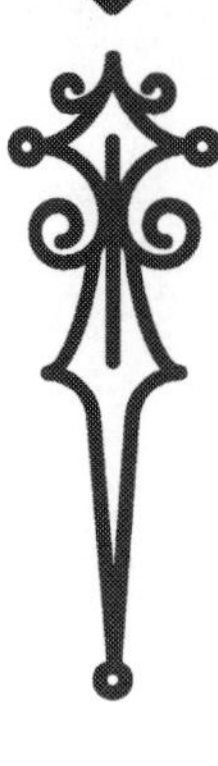

"Dear friend, I pray
that you may enjoy
good health and that
all may go well with
you, even as your
soul is getting along."
3 John 1:2

PRAYER

What is your prayer?
Write your thoughts below.

"Is anyone among you sick?
Let them call the elders
of the church to pray
over them and anoint
them with oil in the
name of the Lord.
And the prayer offered
in faith will make the
sick person well;
the Lord will raise them up.
If they have sinned, they will be
forgiven."

James 5:14–15

PRAYER CHANGES THINGS

Have someone pray with you.

Write your thoughts below.

"My son, pay attention
to what I say;
turn your ear to my words.
Do not let them out
of your sight, keep
them within your heart;
for they are life to
those who find them
and health to one's own body."
Proverbs 4:20–22

THE WORD

What are you paying attention to today? Write your thoughts below.

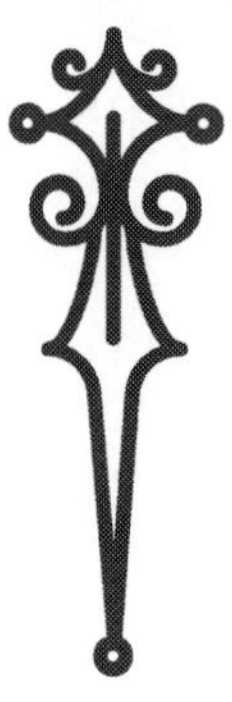

"Worship the Lord your God,
and his blessing
will be on your
food and water.
I will take away
sickness from among you"
Exodus 23:25

WORSHIPING GOD

How will you worship God today?
Write your thoughts below.

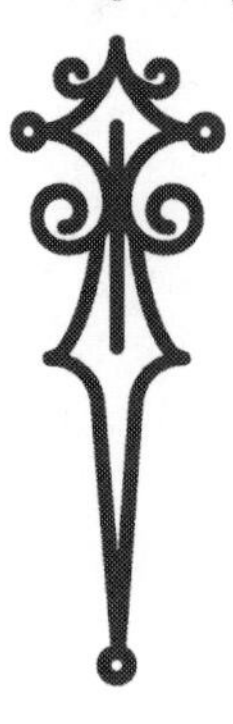

"He sent out his word
and healed them;
he rescued them
from the grave."
Psalms 107:20

THE WORD HEALS

What do you need healed today? Be specific. Write your thoughts below.

"The Lord is my shepherd, I lack nothing. He makes me to lie down in green pastures, he leads me beside quiet waters, he refreshes my soul. He guides me along the right paths for his name's sake."

Psalms 23:1-3

GOD WILL LEAD YOU

Let God lead you and guide you through every decision you will make. Write your thoughts below.

"Even though I walk
through the darkest valley,
I will fear no evil,
for you are with me;
your rod and your
staff comfort me."
Psalms 23:4

GOD IS A COMFORTER

Don't be afraid, God will comfort you.

Write your thoughts below.

"You prepare a table before me
in the presence
of my enemies.
You anoint my
head with oil;
my cup overflows.
Surely your goodness
and love will follow
me all the days of my life,
and I will dwell
in the house of the Lord
forever."

Psalms 23:5-6

GOD WILL PROVIDE

What are you in need of today from God? Write your thoughts below.

"For no matter how many
promises God has made,
they are "Yes" in Christ.
And so through him the
"Amen" is spoken
by us to the
glory of God."
2 Corinthians 1:20

GOD'S PROMISES

What promises are you standing on?
Write your thoughts below.

"A man with leprosy came and knelt before him and said, "Lord, if you are willing, you can make me clean." Jesus reached out his hand and touched the man. "I am willing," he said. "Be clean!" Immediately he was cleansed of his leprosy."

Matthew 8:2-3

AN ENCOUNTER WITH GOD

If you had an encounter with God what would you say? Write your thoughts below.

"This day I call
the heavens and the earth as
witnesses against you that I
have set before you life and
death, blessings and curse.
Now choose life, so that you
and your children may live."

Deuteronomy 30:17

THE OFFER

Before the beginning of time God chose you. Won't you do the same? Write your thoughts below.

"But I will restore you to
health and heal
your wounds,
declares the Lord,
because you
are called
an outcast,
Zion for whom
no one cares."
Jeremiah 30:17

HE RESTORES

What do you want restored?
Write your thoughts below.

"Have faith in God," Jesus
answered. "Truly I tell you, if
anyone says to
this mountain, Go, throw
yourself
into the sea, and does not
doubt in their
heart but believes
that what they
say will happen,
it will be done for them."
Mark 11:22-23

HAVE FAITH

Where is your faith?
Write your thoughts below.

"Therefore I tell you,
whatever you
ask for in prayer,
believe that you
have received it,
and it will be yours."

Mark 11:24

BELIEVE

Ask the Lord for what you want, and believe that you have received it. Write your thoughts below.

"The thief comes only
to steal
and kill
and
destroy;
I have come
that they may
have life,
and have it
to the full."
John 10:10

GOD LOVES YOU

People will come in your life to steal your joy and peace. How will you handle it? Write your thoughts below.

"Let us hold unswervingly
to the hope we
profess, for he
who promised is faithful.
Hebrews 10:23

HOLD ON

Don't give up. God is with you. What are ways you can hold on to your faith? Write your thoughts below.

"Beat your plowshares into
swords and your
pruning
hooks into spears.
Let the weakling say,
"I am strong!"
Joel 3:10

YOU ARE STRONG

How are you feeling today? Ask God for strength. Write your thoughts below.

"This is the confidence we have
in approaching God:
that if we ask anything
according to his will,
he hears us.
And if we know
that he hears us – whatever we
ask – we know that we have
what we asked of him.
1 John 5:14–15

DO NOT BE AFRAID

What do you need today?
Write your thoughts below.

"The weapons we fight with are
not the weapons of the world.
On the contrary, they have
divine power to demolish
strongholds.
We demolish arguments and
every pretension that sets
itself up against the knowledge
of God, and we take captive
every thought to make it
obedient
to Christ.

2 Corinthians 10:4-5

BE POSITIVE

Guard your mind and your thoughts.
Write your thoughts below.

"Finally, be strong
in the Lord
and in his mighty power.
Put on the full armor of God,
so that you can
take your stand
against the devils schemes."
Ephesians 6:10–11

BE PREPARED

You are stronger than you thought.
Always take the word of God with you.
Write your thoughts below.

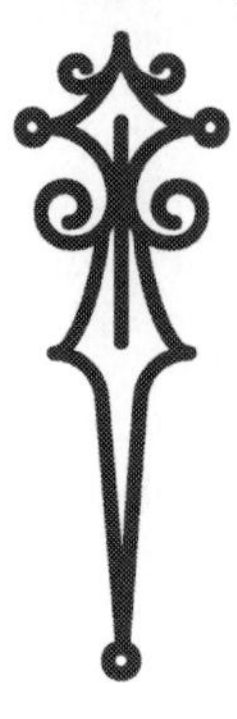

"Heal me, Lord,
and I will be healed;
save me and
I will be saved,
for you are the
one I praise."
Jeremiah 17:14

PRAISE GOD

Take this moment to praise God for your healing. Write your thoughts below.

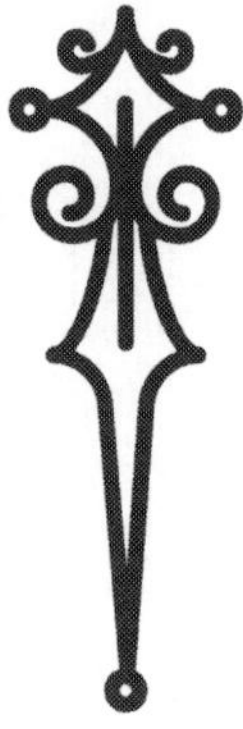

"Gracious words are a honeycomb, sweet to the soul and healing to the bones."

Proverbs 16:24

SPEAK LIFE

Use positive words when you are thinking about your situation. Write your thoughts below.

"the Lord gives sight to the blind,the Lord lifts up those who are bowed down, the Lord loves the righteous."

Psalms 146:8

MIRACLES

God is still performing miracles.
Write your thoughts below.

"He will wipe every tear

from their eyes.

There will be no more

death or mourning

or

crying or pain,

for the old order of things

has passed away."

Revelation 21:4

NO MORE CRYING

God is watching over you.
Write your thoughts below.

"And wherever he went—
into villages, towns or
countryside—they placed the
sick in the marketplaces.
They begged him to let them
touch even the edge of his
cloak, and all who touched it
were healed."

Mark 6:56

GOOD NEWS

Healing is available to everyone.
Write your thoughts below.

"Go back and tell Hezekiah, the ruler of my people, 'This is what the Lord, the God of your father David, says: I have heard your prayer and seen your tears; I will heal you. On the third day from now you will go up to the temple of the Lord."

2 Kings 20:5

GOD HEARS YOU

Your prayers have not fallen on deaf ears.

Write your thoughts below.

"When Jesus came into Peter's house, he saw Peter's mother-in-law lying in bed with a fever. He touched her hand and the fever left her, and she got up and began to wait on him."

Matthew 9:28-30

GRATITUDE

Jesus is just a touch away.
Write your thoughts below.

"But for you who revere my name, the sun of righteousness will rise with healing in its rays. And you will go out and frolic like well-fed calves."

Malachi 4:2

REVERENCE

Open your heart to God.
Write your thoughts below.

"But I want you to know that the Son of Man has authority on earth to forgive sins." So he said to the paralyzed man, "Get up, take your mat and go home." Then the man got up and went home."

Matthew 9:6–7

AUTHORITY

No one is beyond God's help.
Write your thoughts below.

"and the people all tried to touch him, because power was coming from him and healing them all."

Luke 6:19

CLOUDY

Although it might seem cloudy right now. Never doubt Jesus' power to heal. Write your thoughts below.

"So do not fear,

for I am with you;

do not be dismayed,

for I am your God.

I will strengthen you and help

you; I will uphold

you with my

righteous hand."

Isaiah 41:10

GOD IS WITH YOU

He will help you through any situation you are going through. Lean on him. Write your thoughts below.

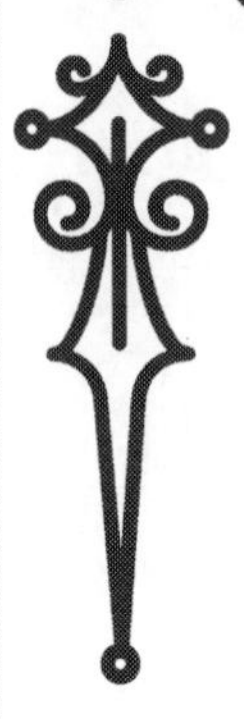

"And my God will
meet all your
needs according
to the riches
of his glory in
Christ Jesus."

Philippians 4:19

GOD WILL MEET YOUR NEEDS

What are lacking today?

Write your thoughts below.

"A cheerful heart
is good medicine,
but a crushed
spirit dries
up the bones."
Proverbs 17:22

BE CHEERFUL

Today is the day that the Lord has made
let us rejoice.
Write your thoughts below.

"Lord be gracious to us;

we long for you.

Be our strength

every morning,

our salvation

in time of distress."

Isaiah 33:2

YOUR ARE MY STRENGTH

Sometimes it is hard to be strong. Ask God for strength.

Write your thoughts below.

"Come to me, all you who are
weary and burdened, and I
will give you rest.
Take my yoke upon you and
learn from me, for I am gentle
and humble in heart, and you
will find rest for your souls.
For my yoke is easy and my
burden is light."
Matthew 11:28-30

REST - RELAX

Give all of your worries and fears to God.
Write your thoughts below.

"He himself bore
our sins" in his
body on the cross,
so that we might
die to sins and live for
righteousness, "by his wounds
you have been healed."
I Peter 2:24

JESUS DIED FOR YOU

Not only did Jesus die for our sins, he died so that we might live again. Won't you trust him?

Write your thoughts below.

"He gives strength
to the weary
and increases
the power
of the weak."
Isaiah 40:29

GOD IS A STRONG TOWER

If you feel like you can't handle it any more, give it to God.

Write your thoughts below.

"Lord my God,
I called to you
for help,
and you healed me."
Psalms 30:2

CALL ON HIM

When you call on him and ask him for help, believe what you have asked for. Write your thoughts below.

"Praise the Lord, my soul,
and forget not all
his benefits – who forgives all
your sins and
heals all your
diseases, who redeems
your life from the pit and
crowns you with love and
compassion"

Psalms 103:2-4

HE REDEEMS

Trust him.
Write your thoughts below.

"Have mercy on me,
Lord, for I am faint;
heal me,
Lord for my
bones are in agony."
Psalms 6:2

I AM FAINT

Continue to put your trust in him.
Write your thoughts below.

"Jesus went through
all the towns and
villages, teaching
in their synagogues,
proclaiming the
good news of the
kingdom and
healing every
disease and sickness."

Matthew 9:35

GOOD NEWS

What good news do you have to share today?

Write your thoughts below.

"He said to her, "
Daughter,
your faith has
healed you.
Go in peace and
be free from
your suffering."
Mark 5:34

YOU ARE FREE

Have faith that God will do what he said he would do. Stand on his word. Write your thoughts below.

"and a woman was there who
had been crippled by a spirit
for eighteen years. She was
bent over and could not
straighten up at all. When
Jesus saw her, he called her
forward and said to her,
'Woman, you are set free from
your infirmity.' Then he put his
hands on her, and immediately
she straightened up and
praised God."

Luke 13:11–13

LISTEN

If he did it for her, he can do it for you.
Write your thoughts below.

"There he found a man named
Aeneas, who was
paralyzed and had been
bedridden for eight years.
'Aeneas,' Peter said to him,
'Jesus Christ heals you. Get
up and roll up your mat.'
Immediately Aeneas got up.."
Acts 9:33-34

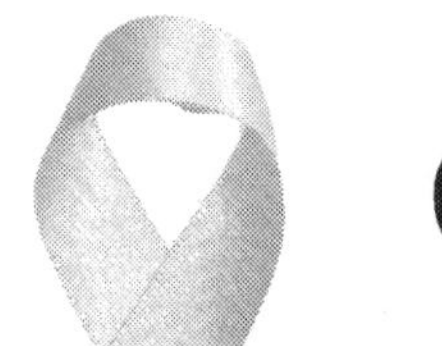

GET UP

Walk in your healing every day.
Write your thoughts below.

"While I am in the world, I
am the light of the world.
After saying this,
he spit on the ground, made
some mud with the saliva, and
put it on the man's eyes. 'Go,'
he told him, 'wash in the Pool
of Siloam.' So the man went
and washed, and came home
seeing."

John 9:5-7

BE OBEDIENT

Follow God. He will not lead you astray.
Write your thoughts below.

"His neighbors and those
who had formerly seen
him begging asked,
'Isn't this the same man
who used to sit and beg?'
Some claimed that he was.
Others said,
'No, he only looks like him.'
But he himself insisted,
'I am the man.'
John 9:8–9

TESTIMONY

Tell the Goodness of the Lord. What has he done for you lately? Write your thoughts below.

"'How then were your
eyes opened?' they asked.
He replied,
'The man they call Jesus
made some mud and put
it on my eyes. He told me
to go to Siloam
and wash So I went
and washed, and then
I could see.'"
John 9:10-11

Tell your story. How has God helped you through your journey?

Write your thoughts below.

"I will not die

but live,

and will

proclaim

what the

Lord has done."

Psalms 118:17

HALLELUJAH

Proclaim his goodness. Meditate on what God has done for you. Write your thoughts below.

"Have I not commanded you?
Be strong and courageous.
Do not be afraid;
do not be discouraged,
for the Lord your God
will be with you
wherever you go."
Joshua 1:9

HAVE COURAGE

No matter what you hear or what you see, remember God will be with you. Write your thoughts below.

"Peace I leave with you;
my peace I give you.
I do not give to you
as the world gives.
Do not let your hearts
be troubled and
do not be afraid."
John 14:27

God wants your heart and mind to be in perfect peace. How can you accomplish that today? Write your thoughts below.

"if my people, who are
called by my name,
will humble themselves
and pray and seek my
face and turn form
their wicked ways,
then I will hear from heaven,
and I will forgive their sin
and will heal their land.
Now my eyes may be
open and my ears attentive
to the prayers offered in this place."

2 Chronicles 7:14–15

SEEK HIS FACE

What sins or things do you need to turn away from to seek God's face? Write your thoughts below.

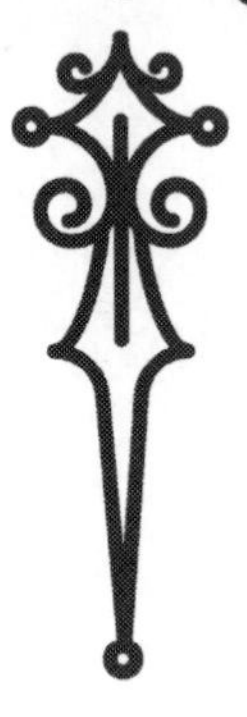

"for it is God

who works

in you to will

and to act

in order to

fulfill his

good purpose ."

Philippians 2:13

GOD LIVES IN YOU

His word will not return void. Trust him.
Write your thoughts below.

"Christ redeemed us from
the curse of the law by
becoming a curse for us,
for it is written,
'Cursed is everyone who
is hung on a pole.'
He redeemed us in order
that the blessing given to
Abraham might come
to the Gentiles through
Christ Jesus, so that by faith we might
receive the promise of the Spirit."
Galatians 3:13–14

STAND

Receive his promises by faith.
Write your thoughts below.

"Therefore confess your sins
to each other
and pray
for each other
so that you
may be healed.
The prayer
of a righteous person
is powerful and effective."
James 5:16

CONFESS

We all need prayer. Who can you pray for? Write your thoughts below.

"Then Jesus said to
the centurion,
'Go! Let it be done just
as you believed it would.'
And his servant was healed at that
moment."
Matthew 8:13

IT IS DONE

Sometimes you have to stand on his word, believe and claim your healing. Can you do that today?

Write your thoughts below.

NOTES...

NOTES...

NOTES...

NOTES...

NOTES...

Made in United States
Orlando, FL
18 December 2021